CW00868063

This
book belongs to

......................................

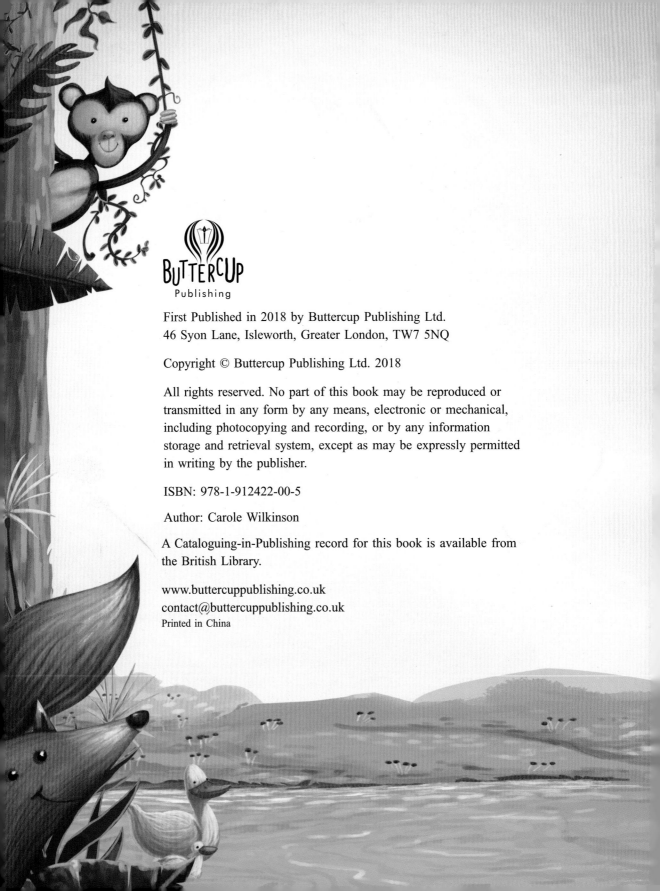

**BUTTERCUP** Publishing

First Published in 2018 by Buttercup Publishing Ltd.
46 Syon Lane, Isleworth, Greater London, TW7 5NQ

Copyright © Buttercup Publishing Ltd. 2018

All rights reserved. No part of this book may be reproduced or transmitted in any form by any means, electronic or mechanical, including photocopying and recording, or by any information storage and retrieval system, except as may be expressly permitted in writing by the publisher.

ISBN: 978-1-912422-00-5

Author: Carole Wilkinson

A Cataloguing-in-Publishing record for this book is available from the British Library.

www.buttercuppublishing.co.uk
contact@buttercuppublishing.co.uk
Printed in China

# 101
## Illustrated
# Animal
## Stories

# The Fox Amongst the Lion's Cubs

One day, a lioness found a fox cub who was shivering and crying from hunger. When she saw that there was no-one to take care of the fox cub, she took him home and raised him with her lion cubs.

The lion cubs treated the fox cub as one of their own and just like one big family, they all grew up together. One day, the lioness took them all out to hunt, but the fox cub was scared, as he didn't know how to hunt and tried to discourage the lion cubs from hunting.

To survive, lions need to hunt for their food and worried that the shy fox would discourage the lion cubs from hunting, she took the fox cub back to his family.

# Biggy and Littlu

Biggy was a huge dinosaur and Littlu was a small dinosaur, but despite the difference in their size, the two were best friends.

One day, Littlu saw that Biggy was sitting with his hands over his ears because they were hurting.

'Let me put some ear-drops into your ears. It will help with the pain,' suggested Littlu.

'That won't help,' moaned Biggy.

'I will get a torch and go inside your ear,' said Littlu, who didn't like to see his friend in pain.

He went inside Biggy's ear and searched high and low, as he walked with his torch. Eventually, he found a spider.

'You're hurting my friend!' said Littlu, to the spider and then picked him up and took him out of Biggy's ear, so that it no longer hurt him.

# The Musical Donkey

There was once a donkey, who worked hard in the fields carrying heavy loads during the day, but was never given enough food to eat. The donkey was good friends with a jackal, who used to give him delicious vegetables to eat.

One night, the jackal took the donkey to a field full of vegetables. 'You need to be quiet, or you'll wake the owner,' advised the jackal. 'Okay,' replied the donkey.

But when the donkey saw all of the delicious cucumbers, he was so happy that he began to sing.

The owner woke up and rushed out, holding a stick and beat the foolish donkey.

'I should have listened,' thought the donkey, as he rubbed his sore back.

# The Wise Old Bird

There was once a gaggle of geese, who lived in a tall tree in the forest. The geese were happy there and had no worries. Then one day, an old, wise goose spotted a creeper growing towards their tree and warned the birds that it was dangerous.

'Don't worry. It won't harm us!' said the foolish geese.

The wise goose tried to warn them, again and again, but they wouldn't listen.

The creeper grew and grew, until one morning, the geese found themselves trapped. They cried out when they realised their mistake. When the wise goose saved them, they vowed to always honour her wisdom.

# The Owl and The Grasshopper

When the sun had set, it was time for the owl to go out hunting, but the owl felt sleepy and couldn't get out of bed.

A grasshopper had been making a noise all day and had disturbed his sleep, so when the owl saw him, he asked him to be a little quieter.

Although the grasshopper agreed, he wasn't quiet and so the next night, the owl was too tired to go hunting.

The owl decided to teach the grasshopper a lesson and when he saw it in the garden, he trapped it in a jar.

'Now you can make as much noise as you like!' yelled the owl, who could now sleep peacefully every day.

# The Mice and
# The Cat

There was once a farmer who was worried because some mice had made their home in his cellar and were eating the grain which was stored in there.

'Get a cat!' advised his wife.

So, the farmer got a cat and soon the mice began to disappear.

The mice became worried and decided to do something about the cat.

'Let's put a bell around the cat's neck. Then we will be able to hear it and save ourselves,' said a mouse.

They all agreed, then an old mouse asked, "Who will put the bell in the cat's neck?' No-one replied as all of them were scared to go near the cat. So they sat down again to think of some other idea to get rid of the cat.

# The Caterpillar Who Did Not Want to Become a Butterfly

There was once a caterpillar who was basking in the sun and listening to the world around him.

'Have you learnt the math's table?' asked a boy.

'Not yet,' replied a girl. 'You have to learn it, so that you can solve math problems when you're older,' said the boy.

The caterpillar was surprised to hear this. Next, he saw two donkeys.

'You have to walk properly,' said the mother donkey.

'Why?' asked the baby donkey.

'So that you can carry heavy loads when you're older,' she replied.

'I don't want to grow up!' exclaimed the caterpillar and then went to sleep. Day after day, people would go and see if the caterpillar had turned into a butterfly. But he hadn't. He didn't want to grow up and become a butterfly.

# The Monkey's Heart

One day, a monkey was sitting on a tree. It decided to have some fun and jumped onto a log floating in the river.

The monkey nearly fell into the river when the log suddenly moved and turned out to be a crocodile.

'Now I will have a monkey's heart to give to my wife!' exclaimed the crocodile.

The monkey was clever and wasn't afraid, as he said, 'Oh, you should have told me that before as I have left my heart on the tree.'

The silly crocodile took the monkey back to the side of the river, so that he could fetch his heart. The monkey leapt onto the bank and escaped. The silly crocodile realised that he had been tricked and swam away, empty handed.

# The Two Goats

There was once a goat named Guessy, who lost track of time. When he realised that the sun was setting, he rushed towards the bridge that would take him home.

He was in such a rush, that he didn't see that there was another goat coming from the opposite direction, until they met each other face to face, on the bridge.

'Get out of my way,' said the goat.

'I'm going to be late,' replied Guessy.

Neither of the two goats wanted to move out of the way. They began to argue and fight. As they fought, they both fell into the river and realised that if any one of them would have stepped aside, they would both be home safely.

# The Town Mouse and The Country Mouse

There was once a town mouse, who went to visit his cousin in the countryside. The country mouse was happy to see him, but the town mouse didn't like the simple lifestyle which his cousin had.

'Come home with me,' he said.

The country mouse was excited, as he had never been to a town and was amazed to see the tall buildings. When the town mouse took him to a house, he saw a table, which was laden with wonderful food. But just as they started to eat it, a woman rushed at them with a broom.

Terrified, the country mouse ran all the way back to his home in the countryside. He felt safer and happier in the countryside and never went back to the town again.

# Tibi Yak Plays
# a Violin

It was holiday time and the sun was shining. A goat named Veronica, was sitting on the green grass and singing, 'It's such a beautiful day. The sky is clean, the grass so green, the breeze so cool, closed is the school.'

Cuty, the buffalo, heard her song and began to dance, which made Veronica laugh.

'I wish someone would play a musical instrument,' said Cuty.

Tibi, the yak, was out walking and had stopped to watch his friends.

'I will go and fetch my violin and then we will have our own musical group,' said Tibi.

Tibi played his violin, whilst Veronica sang and Cuty danced. All three enjoyed their holidays.

# The Monkey Who Couldn't Climb Trees

There was once a kind goat, who had found a baby monkey close to a well and raised him.

One day, when the brother goat and the monkey went into a forest, they came across a berry tree.

'Why don't you get those berries, brother?' asked the goat.

The monkey jumped onto the tree and fell back down. He tried again and again, but he couldn't climb the tree and reach the berries. He was a monkey who couldn't climb trees.

When the other monkeys saw him fall out of the tree, they all laughed and so, the goat and the monkey left empty handed.

# The Turtle and The Swans

There was once a turtle and two swans who were good friends. As their lake was drying up, the swans wwnted to search for another lake to swim in.

The turtle wanted to go with them, but he couldn't fly.

The swans had an idea and said, 'We will put a stick in your mouth and carry the two ends of the stick in our beaks. You will be able to go with us then, but you must remember to keep your mouth closed. Jf you don't, you will fall down and die.'

The turtle agreed and during their journey, they came to a town. All of the people were surprised to see the flying turtle and their noise caught his attention.

He opened his mouth, to ask about the commotion. But just as he opened his mouth, he fell down and died.

# Tuk-tuk The Horse Helps Little Bird

Tuk-Tukthe horse was out for a morning walk, when he heard a strange sound. He stopped walking to listen and discovered that it was the sound of someone crying.

'Who could be crying, so early in the morning?' wondered Tuk-Tuk.

He looked around, to see a little bird hiding under a leaf.

'What's the matter?' asked Tuk-Tuk.

'I was sitting in my nest, when a strong wind blew me out of it. I haven't learnt to fly yet and I don't know how to get back to the nest,' cried the bird.

Tuk-Tuk smiled and said, 'Don't worry. I will help you.'

He picked up the bird and placed him back in the nest.

'Thank you...thank you,' chirped the bird, happily.

21

# The Wise Frog

There were three frogs named, Mandy, Teddy and Sally, who lived in a big pond. Animals from far and wide, would drink water from their pond and share their stories with the frogs.

'It hasn't rained for days. The farmer says that if it doesn't rain soon, then there will be no water,' said a horse.

'I think that we had best start looking for a new pond,' said Teddy.

Mandy and Sally agreed. So, the next morning, they set off early to look for a new pond. They soon came to a well and just as Teddy was about to jump in, Mandy pulled him back. She threw a stone into the well.

'See, there's no water in the well,' said Mandy, when she didn't hear a splash.

So, the frogs walked away, to continue their search for a new pond.

# Dingy Gets Ready for School

Dingy, was a dinosaur, who hated going to school. He was always late waking up and his mother would try everything to get her lazy son to school. But nothing worked.

One day, Dingy was lying on a park bench, when he heard two girls reading out loud. 'How do you know so many things?' asked Dingy.

'From these books,' replied one of the girls and then handed him a book. Dingy read it and found that it was very interesting. He hurried home, to pack his school bag and polish his shoes.

That evening, he had his dinner on time and went to bed. The next morning, he woke up at sunrise and quickly got dressed.

'Where are you off to?' asked his mother, surprised. 'To school,' replied Dingy, happily.

# Veronica Goat Bakes a Cake

It was a cool, sunny afternoon when Veronica and Tuk-Tuk the horse were having tea. 'Have you bought a present for Woolly's baby?' asked Tuk-Tuk.

Veronica shook her head and replied, 'Not yet. I'm still deciding.' Tuk-tuk smiled and said, 'It seems that someone is running out of ideas.'

Veronica laughed. 'It's true. I don't know what to get. I'm going to the gift store. You can come too,' she said. 'Sorry. I can't, I have work to do,' said Tuk-Tuk.

When Tuk-Tuk left, Veronica washed the empty tea-cups.

She looked at the oven and exclaimed, 'I'll make a cake.'

As she had all of the ingredients, she mixed them together and popped the mixture into the oven. Soon, the cake was ready and Veronica decorated it with icing. She smiled. She now had a lovely gift for the baby.

# The Snobbish
# Frog Princess

There was once a Frog Princess who was so snobbish, that the king married her off to a Beggar Frog. The Beggar Frog and the Frog Princess lived in a rundown cottage, far away from the kingdom. The Frog Princess had to sleep on the cold, hard floor, with only a sack for a blanket and she only had berries to eat.

One day, the Beggar Frog took a job as a potter in a neighbouring kingdom and the Frog Princess worked as a cook.

Gradually, the Beggar Frog became cleaner and more jovial and the Frog Princess became less snobbish and more kind-hearted.

Seeing that the Frog Princess had changed, The Beggar Frog revealed that he was really the kingdom's prince.

The Frog Prince and Princess lived happily ever after.

# Woolly Sheep Has a Baby

'Woolly sheep has a baby!' exclaimed Veronica. 'Let's go and see him,' suggested Tibi. On their way to see the baby, they met Tuk-Tuk the horse. 'Where are you going?' he asked. Veronica told him about Woolly sheep's baby. 'I will come with you,' said Tuk-Tuk.

As they were walking, they met Mo the cow, who asked where they were going. 'We're going to see Woolly sheep's baby,' replied Veronica. Mo also joined them and when they arrived, they found that Woolly was resting in bed, with the baby sleeping next to her.

Veronica, Tibi, Tuk-Tuk and Mo were delighted to see the baby. They congratulated Woolly and then kissed the baby.

# The Singing Monkey

There was a monkey, named Mumbo, who wanted to be a singer, but he had a croaky voice. He would sit on the highest branch of the trees and sing as loud as he could, which irritated the animals.

One day, a lion invited Mumbo to dinner, to honour his singing. He also invited Panther and Tiger.

During dinner, the lion asked Mumbo to sing. The monkey proudly sang in his croaky voice.

'Louder...louder!' growled Panther, flashing her sharp teeth.

'Come on, sing!' growled Tiger, flashing his sharp teeth.

The lion growled too. Mumbo was so scared, that when he tried to sing, he couldn't. Terrified, he ran out of the lion's den and no-one ever heard him singing again.

# The Sly Crow

There was once a parrot and a crow, who were best friends, although the parrot was kind and helpful, whereas the crow was sly and cunning.

The crow only thought of herself and her welfare. Even though the parrot knew this, she chose to believe that the crow would change.

One day, the parrot built a nest and laid her eggs in it. But when the parrot flew off to find food, the crow removed the parrot's eggs and laid her eggs in it.

The sly crow had thought that her babies would look like the parrot's. It wasn't long before the parrot realised that the babies were not hers, but belonged to the crow. She felt betrayed and was then sad to realise that the crow would never change.

# Baby Lamb's First Winter

It was the first winter for the baby lambs, Daisy and Mini. Their mother gave them both a bowl of cheese balls and popcorn, while she read them a story about Antarctica.

The lambs were astonished to hear about Eskimos and the huskies, who pulled sledges laden with goods.

'The igloos are houses made from blocks of ice,' said their mother.

'We want to go to Antarctica,' exclaimed Daisy and Mini, as they jumped on the couch.

'Well, South Island is a lot like Antarctica,' said their mother and pointed at the window.

The baby lambs could see that it was snowing. They ran outside shouting, 'Weeee!'

They all went outside and together, they made a snowman.

# Disci Goes to Disco

'Mamma. Why is my name Disci?' asked Disci the dinosaur.'Your Aunt Pisci named you Disci. She loved to go to the disco and she loved you too,' replied her mother.

'What is a disco?' she asked.

'It's a place where people dance to loud music,' said her mother.

Disci decided to go to a disco, to see what it was like and took her friend, Littlu with her.

They wore their best dresses, but when the doorman saw them, he shook his head.

'Sorry! Children are not allowed,' he said.

So, Disci and Littlu stood with their noses pressed against the window. They watched everyone dance and thought it was wonderful.

# Biggy Helps Alley

There was an elephant named Alley. She was very curious and even though her curiosity often landed her in trouble, this didn't change her.

One day, Biggy the dinosaur found Alley inside a pit. 'How did you fall into the pit?' asked Biggy. 'I jumped inside, to see how it feels...I've never been inside a pit,' said Alley.

'How silly of you,' exclaimed Biggy, who was a big, strong dinosaur, 'Hold my hand tightly and I will pull you out.'

Alley held onto his hand as Biggy pulled her out of the pit. 'Thank you, Biggy!' cried Alley and gave him a big hug.

That evening, she cooked Biggy a wonderful supper, to say thank you to her dear friend.

# Baby Bug's Picnic

One summer's morning, the mummy bugs decided to give their babies a wonderful surprise. They got their food hampers ready and took them out for a picnic.

The baby bugs began to play together and were having a lovely time. Soon the mummy bugs joined in, but the baby bugs weren't playing fairly.

The mummy bugs decided to teach them a lesson, as they wanted them to have good moral values. They wanted the babies to understand how to play fairly, but it wasn't long before all of the baby bugs were crying.

They were no longer having fun. A fairy appeared and helped the baby bugs to understand, that their mummies only wanted what was best for them.

Realising this, the baby bugs joined in the play with their mummies once again.

# Cluck-Cluck Hen Learns to Count

Cluck-Cluck the hen was walking around, with her eggs in her pocket. 'How many chicks will hatch from your eggs?' asked Tuk-Tuk the horse.

'As many as there are eggs,' replied Cluck-Cluck. 'Tell me in numbers. How many chicks?' asked Tuk-Tuk.

'In numbers!' said Cluck-Cluck, confused.

'Put the eggs on the ground and count them. Then you will know how many,' said Tuk-Tuk.

'I don't know how to count,' said Cluck-Cluck, dismayed.

'Count your beak. One,' said Tuk-Tuk.

'One beak!' said Cluck-Cluck, touching her beak.

'Count your eyes. Two,' said Tuk-Tuk.

This was the way that Tuk-Tuk helped Cluck-Cluck to learn how to count.

# The Two Crows

One day, there were two crows named Toasty and Sade who decided to have a competition. They wanted to see who could carry a bag into the sky, the highest. The winner would then be able to eat Uncle Crow's tasty pie.

The two crows prepared for the competition. Toasty filled his bag with cotton and Sade filled his with salt. On the day of the competition, all of the animals gathered to watch them.

Toasty and Sade flew up into the sky, with their bags. Suddenly, it started to rain. Toasty felt his bag grow heavier and couldn't fly any more. The rain had melted the salt in Sade's bag and it felt lighter. He flew higher and higher and was declared the winner, although he did share the pie with Toasty.

# The Two
# Frogs

The was once a She frog and a He frog who lived on the same island, but had never seen each other. One day, they were bored of their surroundings and decided to explore the island.

She frog set off for the north side and He frog set off for the south side. They were both surprised, when they bumped into each other. They chattered and soon became friends.

They had many more adventures together, as they travelled across the island. They discovered new places and made new friends.

Days passed and they enjoyed each other's company. So much so, that they fell in love and were soon married.

# Boo Dog Cleans His Home

Aunt Carrey sent a parcel of goodies to Boo Dog, as he was her favourite nephew. Boo Dog wanted to share his goodies with his friends and decided to invite them to his tea party.

He went to give his friends their invitations, but they all turned him down. Boo Dog was sad and sat under a tree. Cluck-Cluck saw him and asked, 'Why are you sad?'

'No-one wants to come to my party,' cried Boo Dog.

'Nobody wants to go to an unclean and untidy house. Why don't you clean your home and then invite them again,' suggested Cluck-Cluck.

Boo Dog thought that it was a great idea. He cleaned his home and then invited all of his friends. This time, they all said, 'Yes!'

# Lazy Pingu

Pingu was a lazy, little penguin. He always delayed doing his tasks and whenever his parents tried to explain the importance of finishing his tasks early, he didn't listen.

One day, Pingu's class teacher had decided to take the students for a picnic. Everyone needed to be in the school on time.

Pingu and his friends were excited, but when Pingu reached home, he didn't take off his uniform, he didn't pack his picnic bag and he didn't polish his shoes. He left all of his tasks, to do them in the morning.

But the next morning, Pingu woke up late. He couldn't make it to the school on time and he missed the picnic. He learnt a valuable lesson...Not to delay any of his tasks again.

# Devil of the Seaweeds

Two jellyfish, named Pinata and Limci, were on one of their excursions. 'Let's explore the back of our house,' suggested Limci.

They swam about, looking for interesting and colourful shells. 'Look, a jungle!' cried Pinata. They went inside some dense seaweed, where it was very dark. 'I'm scared. Let's go back,' whispered Limci.

Suddenly, they heard a noise, coming from inside a cave. They peeped inside to find a small creature staring back at them. 'A devil!' screamed Limci.

The creature opened its mouth, showing long, sharp, fang-like teeth. It rushed at them. They ran back to their mother and told her what had happened.

'It was a fang tooth fish. It has really sharp teeth and lives in caves,' said their mother. Pinata and Limci were relieved that it wasn't a devil after all.

# Mo Cow Knits a Pullover

On a bright and cheerful morning, Mo Cow was sitting on her porch and reading her newspaper. Her little calf, Bobsy, ran over to her.

'Mom, J'm feeling cold!' said Bobsy and then jumped into bed, covering himself with a quilt. But he soon became bored. Mo called Cuty. 'Bobsy wants to play outside, but he's feeling cold. What should J do?'

'Give him a pullover,' replied Cuty. 'Oh, he doesn't have one!' exclaimed Mo and then thought, 'J will knit Bobsy a pullover.'

She gathered some wool from Woolly, sat on the porch and knitted a pullover for Bobsy.

'Now you won't feel cold,' she said. Bobsy smiled. He loved his new pullover.

# Dolly Delivers a Letter

Dolly was a helpful dolphin, who lived in the ocean. One day, she saw that Mrs. Whale was sad, because she was missing her friend who lived on the beach.

'Why don't you write her a letter?' asked Dolly, 'I will go and deliver it to Myra.' 'What a wonderful idea!' said Mrs. Whale, as she hugged Dolly.

So, Mrs. Whale wrote the letter and gave it to Dolly, along with a map, to show her how to reach Pearl Beach where Myra lived.

It took Dolly two days to reach the beach, but she gave the letter to Myra and was given hugs and kisses as a thank you, for reuniting the two friends.

# An Innocent Monkey and a Cunning Alligator

There was a monkey and an alligator who were good friends. They would share stories about the tree-birds and water-animals with each other. The alligator had told his wife all about his monkey friend.

One day, it was the alligator's wife's birthday. 'Dear, what gift would you like for your birthday?' he asked his wife, 'Ask for anything and I will get it for you.' The wife was greedy and cunning and replied, 'I want to eat a monkey's brain.'

'We live in water. How can I get a monkey's brain for you?' asked the confused alligator.

'Get me the brain from your monkey-friend, otherwise I will assume that you don't love me,' said his wife.

The alligator was bewildered, but went to his monkey-friend and said, 'I will take you to an ocean-fairy who will tell you the most wonderful stories.'

The monkey was overjoyed and happily sat on the alligator's back, unaware that his end was near.

# Olivia's Engagement Party

In the ocean, all of the creatures were excited to hear that Olivia, the octopus was to be engaged to Fred, the sea turtle. They had heard that Fred had prepared a blue theme for the special engagement.

Everyone was excited as they hadn't been to an engagement party for a while. They all bought gifts and cards.

On the day of the engagement, everyone reached the venue, to see that Olivia was wearing a pretty pink dress. She wore two beautiful clips and looked lovely. Fred wore a blue bow tie and looked very smart.

Olivia and Fred exchanged rings and then led everyone onto the dance floor. Everyone had a lovely time and remembered the party for a long time.

# There is Always a Way

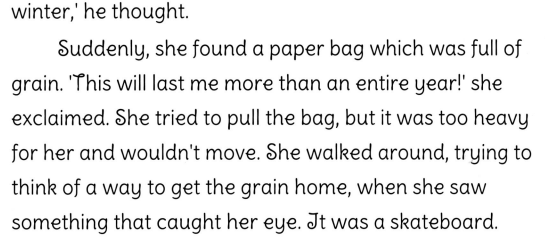

As winter approached, Arnie the ant was looking for food. 'Just a few more rounds then I'm all done for winter,' he thought.

Suddenly, she found a paper bag which was full of grain. 'This will last me more than an entire year!' she exclaimed. She tried to pull the bag, but it was too heavy for her and wouldn't move. She walked around, trying to think of a way to get the grain home, when she saw something that caught her eye. It was a skateboard.

She pushed the skateboard under the bag and then, with all her might, she managed to get the bag of grain onto the skateboard. She pushed it all the way home and had a comfortable winter. When the summer returned, Arnie went out once again, to collect food for the next winter.

# The Wise Decision

It hadn't rained for weeks and the jungle's only watering hole was slowly drying up, so the lion called all of the jungle animals together for a meeting.

'We need to use the water wisely, until we find a new watering hole,' said the lion and then put the animals into groups.

The animals headed in different directions, to look for water. The sun was very hot and after walking for miles, they came across a watering hole. As they all wanted to drink the water at the same time, they began to argue.

Sitting on the branch of a tree was a vulture, who was eagerly watching them.

Seeing this, the lion said, 'Let's stop fighting and drink the water, one by one.'

The animals agreed and soon their thirst was quenched.

# Mystery of the Missing Shell

Limci and Pinata, were two jellyfish who loved to explore the sea-bed.

One day, when they were out exploring, Limci shouted, 'Pinata, come here quick!' Seeing a beautiful shell in Limci's hand, Pinata said, 'It's so beautiful.'

They took the shell home and placed it on the study table. That night, they turned off the table lamp and went to sleep.

The next morning, the shell was nowhere to be seen.

'I think someone has stolen it,' said Limci, as she pointed to an open window.

The two sisters were sad. But then they heard a strange sound coming from their refrigerator. When they opened it, they saw a hermit crab grinning at them, from under the missing shell.

'I live inside this shell,' said the hermit crab. The two sisters apologised. They hadn't realised that the shell could be someone's home.

# The Wolf and
# The Lamb

One day, there was a hungry wolf who was searching for food. He walked to the end of the forest, towards a village.

'Sheep...I hear sheep!' exclaimed the wolf. He ran towards the sound and saw a lamb. His mouth watered, as his stomach rumbled.

'Little lamb...little lamb,' he called. The lamb looked at the wolf and asked, 'What?'

'There is fresh grass here for you to nibble,' said the wolf, as he tried to lure it to him. The sheep knew that the wolf meant to harm him and said, 'No thanks, I have enough grass here.'

The wolf tried to call the lamb again, but the lamb ran away, so the wolf had to go back to the forest, while his tummy continued to rumble.

# Cuty Buffalo Wears a Skirt

Cuty Buffalo was going to a party. 'What should I wear to the party?' she asked Woolly the sheep. 'Show me your dresses and I will help you to decide,' replied Woolly.

So, Cuty took out all of her dresses and laid them on the bed. Woolly sat on the sofa and watched Cuty, as she modelled the different dresses.

Woolly didn't like any of them and said, 'Why don't you wear my skirt for the party? You will look really pretty in it.'

Cuty loved the idea, even though she had never worn a skirt before. That night, at the party, Cuty looked lovely in the skirt.

# The Book Under the Stone

Tiara, the starfish and Humpty, the seahorse were good friends and always played together. One day, they were having a race and decided to have a rest. They sat down near a stone.

'There's something underneath the stone,' said Humpty and then picked up the stone. 'It's a book! It has plastic pages!' said Tiara, as she touched the book.

Tiara and Humpty looked at all of the colourful pictures. Humpty found some pictures of stars and looked at Tiara in disbelief.

'You look like a star,' said Humpty, which made Tiara smile. They were so engrossed in the book, that they ran out of time. But now, whenever they become bored, they look through their special book.

# The Cat Who Was Afraid of Mice

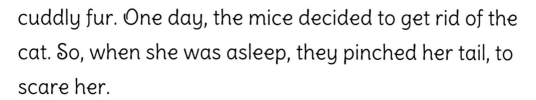

In a storehouse, there lived three mice. They were jealous of a cat named Kitty, who was cute and had soft, cuddly fur. One day, the mice decided to get rid of the cat. So, when she was asleep, they pinched her tail, to scare her.

'We will bite off your tail and then you will be a cat without a tail,' they said.

'But I love my tail!' exclaimed Kitty.

'We will make a brush out of your tail and use it to paint the walls,' said one mean mouse.

Kitty ran to hide, as they sang out, 'Tail! Tail! Tail! We will bite Kitty's tail with our sharp teeth.'

Terrified, Kitty wound some blue yarn around her tail, to disguise it. Afraid of the mice, she always stayed alert.

# The Helpful Rabbit

Mezzo was a very humble and kind rabbit. When he was at school, he would help his friends and at home, he would help his dad in the vegetable garden. At dinnertime, he helped his mum to set out the plates and glasses on the table.

One day, when Mezzo was walking to school, he heard a frightened, 'chirp!' He saw that a baby bird had fallen out of its nest. He put the bird back in its nest.

While he was playing with his friends, he saw some hunters. He tried to warn his friends, but fell into a trap. Eventually, he managed to escape and was running home when he came across the hunter's son, who was crying.

Being kind, Mezzo helped him. The son was grateful and promised not to hunt again and to be kind to all of the animals.

# The Intelligent Lamb

One day, there was a little lamb who had strayed from its flock. A wolf saw the lamb and pounced on it. The lamb tried to get away, but the wolf was big and strong.

'Before you eat me, I have one last wish,' cried the lamb.

'What is your wish?' asked the curious wolf.

'Please, sing me a song,' requested the lamb. So, the wolf sang.

'You have a lovely voice,' said the lamb. The wolf proudly puffed out his chest and sang louder.

A shepherd heard the wolf and ran at it, with a large stick. He beat it black and blue, while the clever lamb ran back to the flock.

# The Inside Story of Clown Fish

One day, Jester, the clown fish was caught in a net and found himself in a pet shop. There were lots of different fish and he was put into a fish tank, next to a goldfish.

A boy knocked on Jester's tank, which scared him. He dashed to the back of the tank and hid behind some coral.

'Mom, I want this one. It's funny,' said the boy.

It wasn't long before Jester found himself in a new home, where he was given food particles to eat. But Jester felt homesick. The boy felt sorry for Jester and decided to put him back into the sea. His father helped him to carefully drop Jester into the water.

Jester happily swam home and was careful not to get caught in a net again.

# The Bear Who Wanted to Make His Own Honey

Miski, the squirrel, was a new student and Gumpi, the bear wanted to be friends with her. Miski had a wonderful, red pencil box, which Gumpi wanted. He tried everything to be friends with her.

He wanted to play on the swings with her. He wanted to give her chocolates and tell her a story about a flying carpet. But she always said, 'No.'

Gumpi thought and thought and then one day, he gave her a honey sandwich, which she loved.

'If I make a jar of honey, especially for you, will you give me your red pencil box?' asked Gumpi. 'Yes,' replied Miski.

Gumpi immediately went to the bees...to learn how to make honey.

# Bumble
# The Honeybee

It was springtime and Queen Bee had laid her eggs. Bumble and all of the worker bees had been assigned their duties.

Highlighted on the duty rota, Bumble was to attend to the queen, who was thrilled. Bumble gave the queen a sponge bath and helped her into her silver gown.

By the time the queen was ready, the babies were awake. Bumble fed them and then served the queen her supper.

She wished the queen a good night and then went onto her next assignment. At the end of the day, she was hungry after her hard day's work. She drank some nectar and then flew into the garden to enjoy the fresh air, before she resumed her work, collecting pollen.

# Posty Quail and Christmas Time

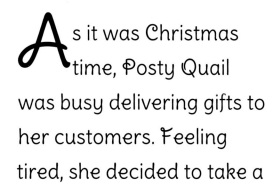

As it was Christmas time, Posty Quail was busy delivering gifts to her customers. Feeling tired, she decided to take a break and was just about to move when the phone rang.

'Hello, Posty from the gift shop,' she answered.

'Please deliver a doll with red hair to my cousin,' said Blacky Crow and then gave Posty the address.

Posty took a sip of coffee and the phone rang again.

It was Dingy Dove, who said, 'Posty, please send a chocolate cake to my friend, Pingu Penguin.'

Posty often gave gift ideas to her customers, who were always happy with her service.

But now that it was the afternoon, she had plans to spend Christmas with her grandma, so she quickly finished her work.

# Mischievous Donkey

The donkey was the most mischievous animal on the farm. He played jokes on all of his friends and would swap their food without them knowing.

The cow was surprised to find carrots instead of hay. The goats were surprised to find hay instead of carrots. The donkey would laugh when he saw their expressions. But one day, the farmer decided to teach the donkey a lesson.

He gave the donkey some green apples and the horse had some red apples. The donkey greedily gobbled up the green apples. He didn't like the sour taste, but he didn't say a word and he never played tricks on his friends again.

# Three Mice and
# The Cat

One day, Kitty the cat, decided to scare the mice who lived in the same building as she did.

'If I can trap the mice, then I can eat them too,' she thought. She decided to lay out a net trap, for the mice, in the lobby.

She was sure that they would be caught and then she would have a sumptuous meal. The cat was right and the mice were soon caught.

She was proud of herself and decided to tell all of her friends about her success, before eating the mice. But while she was doing this, the clever mice used their sharp, pointed teeth to tear a hole in the net.

When the cat arrived home, she saw the hole. Suddenly, the mice ran behind her and bit her tail. She cried for help as she ran away.

# The Sparrow and The Kingfisher

There were a group of birds who lived in a tree, next to a river. A kingfisher would come to the river every day and a little sparrow would watch in awe, as it dived into the river and came back up with a fish. She did not like having to fly everywhere to look for food.

'Why can't we fish, like the kingfisher?' she asked her friends. They laughed and said, 'We are different and our food is different.' 'They're just scared of the water,' thought the sparrow and decided that she would be just like the kingfisher.

The sparrow flew high into the air and then dived down. She tumbled through the air and landed in the river. Her friends helped her out of the river and she learnt that imitating others, could cause her to injure herself.

# Cuty and the Little Bird

Cuty Buffalo was grazing in the green meadow, when she found a little bird crying.

'Dear, what's the matter?' she asked.

'I can't take part in the singing competition, because I have a sore throat,' cried the little bird.

'Don't cry. You can take part in the competition next year,' said Cuty.

The little bird stopped crying and said, 'Yes and I will win too.'

Cuty nodded and said, 'Definitely and you will be able to prepare for it.'

The little bird was no longer sad and thanked Cuty. They became good friends and Cuty would encourage the little bird to practice her singing, ready for the next competition.

# Tina Goes to a Party

Tina was a very rare bird. She was very shy and didn't have any friends. An owl had often seen her and wondered why she was always alone. So one day, he decided to talk to her.

'Hello! I live in this tree,' said the owl.

Tina smiled shyly, as she looked at the owl, feeling too shy to say anything.

'Let's walk together and talk,' suggested the owl.

He talked to her while they walked and soon they became friends. The owl invited her to another bird's party and she accepted. She was very excited when the owl introduced her to all of his friends.

'Welcome, Tina!' shouted everyone.

They all danced and sang. Tina enjoyed the party and made lots of friends there.

# Farm Adventure

It was the time of summer holidays. Mark and Ann were visiting their cousin, Mary, who lived in the countryside. They were excited to spend the holidays at the sheep farm.

Mary showed them around the farm. They had never seen so many sheep before. Some had horns and some didn't have horns. Some had a woolly coat and some didn't.

Mark and Ann wanted to see how the sheep were sheared and so the farmer showed them. He even talked to them about other things which happened on the farm.

The children enjoyed their day and that evening, they ran into the house to change their clothes. Then they had fresh lemon juice and ginger cake. For supper, Mary's dad had cooked roasted lamb, which they all loved.

# Stinky Skunk is Now Happy

Stinky Skunk was feeling sad. 'Everyone runs away from me because I smell,' he thought, dismayed.

A sparrow tried to make Stinky happy.

'I don't like my stink...it makes everyone run away from me,' cried Stinky.

The sparrow smiled and said, 'You should be proud of your smell. It saves you from predators.'

He realised that his natural stink was actually helpful to him.

Stinky nodded and said, 'Thank you. I am grateful to you and really happy now.'

# The Lazy Snake

Winter was approaching and the squirrels were busy gathering nuts. Every day, they would come across a lazy snake, who was always sleeping. The squirrels advised the snake to prepare for winter, but the snake never listened.

The squirrels worked hard to collect their nuts and had filled their storehouse. They were content and chattered about their secret nut store.

The lazy snake was pretending to sleep and listened to their conversation. Then one night, when he couldn't find any food to eat, he raided the squirrel's storehouse.

As he greedily swallowed the nuts, his stomach swelled, until he became trapped in the storehouse. The next morning, the squirrels found him and took him to the Forest Police Station.

# Little Bunny in Trouble

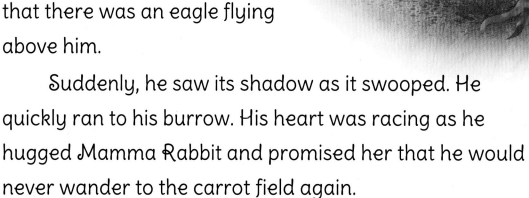

One day, when Mamma Rabbit was away, Little Rabbit crept out of the burrow and ran into a nearby carrot field. He was so busy munching on the carrots, that he didn't notice that there was an eagle flying above him.

Suddenly, he saw its shadow as it swooped. He quickly ran to his burrow. His heart was racing as he hugged Mamma Rabbit and promised her that he would never wander to the carrot field again.

Mamma Rabbit was happy that he was safe and hugged him back. Then, Mamma Rabbit gave him the juicy carrots that she had been collecting. They both enjoyed eating the delicious carrots together.

# Guglu and The Magic Lamp

One day, Guglu, the clownfish, came across a strange lamp. 'Why is there a lamp at the bottom of the sea?' he wondered. The lamp was covered in algae, so Guglu rubbed it.

Suddenly, a white cloud appeared from the lamp. 'I live inside the lamp!' said the creature. Guglu was astonished and asked, 'What do you want?'

'To grant you a wish,' replied the creature. 'I don't have any wish,' said Guglu, surprised.

'Please, you are my master now. When I grant you a wish, I will be free from the lamp,' begged the creature.

Guglu felt sorry for the creature and made a wish, which set the creature free.

# The Monkeys and The Caps

Once, there was a cap-seller who'd had a long and tiring day. Feeling exhausted, he decided to rest under a big tree. He covered his face with a cap and fell asleep.

A group of monkeys lived in the tree and when they saw him sleeping, they decided to investigate. They found a bag full of caps, next to the sleeping cap-seller.

They took the caps and sat in the tree. When the cap-seller woke up, he was surprised to find that his bag was empty. 'Where are my caps?' he murmured.

He heard the monkey's excited chatter and looked up, to see that they were wearing his caps. 'Give me my caps!' shouted the cap-seller. But the monkeys imitated him and made gestures with their hands.

The cap-seller took off his cap and threw it on the ground. The monkeys did the same. The clever cap-seller laughed and scooped up his caps.

# The Lion Who Did Not Want to be King of the Jungle

One morning, Zafar, the lion woke up. He thought about doing something different, as he didn't want to be the King of the Jungle. He wanted to swim in the cool waters of the rushing river.

He wanted to bask in the sun without a care in the world. He wanted friends and he didn't want the animals to be scared of him.

So, he went swimming, then he napped in the sun and made friends with the deer and rabbits. He enjoyed his day and all of the animals were amazed to see how much, the King of the Jungle had changed.

They soon realised that Zafar really wanted to be friends with all of the animals. So now, Zafar and the animals are friends and live together peacefully.

# Baby Rabbit and the Shadow

One bright sunny day, a baby rabbit named, Cotton, was playing in a field when it saw that something dark and wearing horns was following him. Cotton ran around and cried with fear.

'Hey, what's the matter?' asked Papa Rabbit.

'There's a monster behind me,' cried Cotton.

'There's no monster. It's just your shadow,' replied Papa Rabbit.

'Shadow! What's that?' asked Cotton.

'On bright, sunny days, when there's a lot of light, then we get shadows,' said Papa Rabbit.

He took Cotton back to the field and pointed to his shadow.

'Monster!' exclaimed Cotton.

'No, that's your shadow,' said Papa Rabbit.

# The Bird and the Hemp Seeds

In a village, there was a tree where a flock of birds lived. They were noisy and disturbed the villagers. One day, a swallow saw a farmer sowing some seeds under the tree.

'Oh, it's hemp seeds!' exclaimed the swallow and then flew to warn the birds.

'Ah, nothing will happen,' said the birds.

Every day, the farmer would sow the seeds and the birds would eat them. They didn't notice that the farmer had set up a net.

Then, one morning, the birds were trapped in the net and couldn't get out. The swallow saw them and helped them to escape.

'Thank you,' said all of the birds.

# The Ant and The Chrysalis

There was once an ant who found a chrysalis and thought, 'Oh, what a fellow! It looks so dull and sleeps all the time.' The ant would walk past the chrysalis every day and say the same thing. Then one day, the chrysalis was gone.

While the ant was wondering where it had gone, it saw a big, beautiful butterfly flying around. 'I am the chrysalis,' it said.

The ant was very surprised, but realised that appearances can sometimes be deceptive. He thought that the butterfly was beautiful and apologised for his earlier words. He was forgiven and the two became good friends.

# Leggy Emu Wins a Prize

There was once a race, in the Kingdom of Birds. All of the birds participated, to see who could run the fastest. Ooty, the owl was the judge.

Peacocks, parrots, swallows and turkeys ran. So did the emus and ostriches. Some of the birds were good, but some only ran half way and then flew the rest of the way. The final race was between the emu and the ostrich.

During the race, the ostrich hurt her foot and slowed down, so the emu won the race.

'Leggy Emu is the winner!' declared the owl, as he handed her the trophy.

# Donkey's Talent

The farm animals covered their ears and cried, 'Donkey...Stop!'

'Why? I love to sing,' said donkey.

'But your voice is too horrible,' cried the hens.

The donkey wasn't hurt by their words, although he decided to sing at night instead.

One night, when he was out walking and singing in the moonlight, he saw three robbers trying to break into the farmhouse.

The donkey sang loudly, to wake up the farmer. The farmer ran out of the farmhouse and saw the robbers running away.

He thanked the donkey and gave him three juicy apples for alerting him.

# Picnic at the Farm

Jt was a long weekend and the animals were extremely bored.

Veronica Goat had an idea and said, 'Why don't we have a picnic?'

'That's a great idea,' said Moo Cow.

All of the animals were told about the picnic. They packed all of their clothes and headed to the farm's pond, carrying their umbrellas.

Veronica Goat greeted them. Some of the animals jumped into the pond, while some lay on their backs, under the umbrellas, to bask in the sun.

Some munched on pies, cakes and sandwiches, which had been made for the picnic. Some of them played with a ball and they all had a wonderful time.

# The Bird Who Did Not Want to Live in a Nest

There was a bird, named Chinky, who was worried. She didn't want anything to happen to the eggs which she had laid. She had seen a cat, hiding in a nearby bush, ready to pounce on the eggs and wanted to move them to a safer place.

'I cannot keep the eggs in the stable or the shed. The cows and horses will trample on them,' she thought. Roxy, the dog, gave her a tray and said, 'You can keep your eggs on here.'

Chinky put the eggs on the tray, but they rolled around it. 'This is not safe at all!' she cried. Chinky didn't want to live in her nest anymore and wandered around, looking for a safer place.

# The Stupid Jackal

There was a jackal and a camel who were good friends. One day, they decided to cross a deep river. The jackal climbed onto the camel's back and they reached the other side safely.

They saw a field full of sugarcane and gobbled it all up. Suddenly, the jackal howled. 'Keep quiet, you fool! The farmer will come out and beat us!' exclaimed the camel.

'Oh, but I always howl after a wonderful meal,' said the jackal. The farmer rushed out of the farmhouse and beat them both. They ran to the river. Half way across the river, the camel began to sink below the water.

'What are you doing? I will drown!' shouted the jackal. 'Oh, I always take a dip in the river after a lovely meal,' replied the camel. The poor jackal slipped from the camel's back and struggled to stay afloat in the river.

# The Lost Jewel

'Today is the day when I want to test the talents of my dear subjects.' said the Lion King. All the animals were excited and ready. 'A precious jewel has been hidden in the grapevine. Whoever finds it first, will be my principle advisor,' declared the Lion King.

The rabbit reached the grapevine, he could see the jewel, but couldn't climb high enough to reach it. The baby elephant tried, but couldn't reach it either.

Next, the fox tried. He climbed higher and higher, until he grabbed the jewel. Then, he fell asleep in the shade of the grapevine.

The rabbit saw the jewel by the side of the fox and picked it up. He jumped his way to victory and when the fox woke, he could do nothing, except moan about the lost jewel.

# Twin Bears

There were two bears, named Eddie and Murphy, who lived in the forest. Winter was fast approaching and the bears would soon be sleeping.

The bears wanted to have a big feast before they started their hibernation and wandered through the forest.

They walked towards the river and saw that there were a lot of men who were fishing for salmon. On the riverbank, there were buckets full of fish, with no-one guarding them.

While the fishermen were busy catching the fish, Eddie and Murphy crept through the trees and bushes, until they were within arm's reach of the buckets.

They grabbed two buckets of fish and ran back to their cave, where they enjoyed their wonderful feast.

# The Monkeys and The Goat

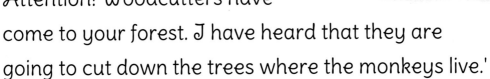

One day, there was a goat who ran to the forest and announced, 'Attention! Attention! Woodcutters have come to your forest. I have heard that they are going to cut down the trees where the monkeys live.'

All of the monkeys were anxious and shrieked, 'What! Now what shall we do? Where will we go?'

One of the monkeys was clever and asked the goat, 'Will you help us, dear friend?'

The goat agreed and they thought of a plan. They crept close to the woodcutters who were just about to cut down the first tree.

The goat leapt from behind and bit the woodcutter's leg. He shrieked in pain, as the axe fell to the floor.

The monkey grabbed the axe and climbed up the first tree that he saw. Their plan had worked and now the monkeys were safe.

# A Rabbit in the Sack

One day, there was a rabbit who was trapped inside a sack. He tried to scratch a hole into it, to escape, but the fabric was too thick.

When the rabbit realised that the sack was full of carrots, his mouth watered. The rabbit noisily ate the carrots. The farmer, who was walking past, heard the noise.

He knew that there was something inside of the sack, so he untied it. The rabbit jumped out and ran away as fast as it could. The farmer could do nothing but watch. The rabbit had taken as many carrots as he could manage to carry and thanked his lucky stars that he had been trapped in a sack full of carrots.

# The Boastful Parrot

There was once a parrot who was very proud and would boast, 'I am the most beautiful bird in the forest.'

This made all of the birds weary of him. One day, when it began to rain, all of the birds flew to the ground and chattered excitedly. The parrot wondered what the birds were up to and also flew down to the ground.

Once there, he saw the most magnificent creature that he had ever seen. It was a peacock, dancing in the rain. All of the birds admired his beauty. But the peacock didn't boast, which made the parrot feel ashamed.

He stood with the other birds and admired the peacock. He never boasted again and became more gentle with the others.

# The Ant and The Turtle

Once there was an ant and a turtle who were friends. They had been falling apart over the past few days and the ant thought that inviting the turtle for dinner would help to rekindle their friendship.

The ant asked the turtle to wash his hands, but every time the turtle went to the dining table, his hands were dirty. The ant grew tired of waiting for the turtle to wash his hands properly and ate all of the food.

After a couple of days, the turtle invited the ant to dinner. The ant wore a jacket, which he filled with stones so that he wouldn't float away.

The turtle asked the ant to take off his jacket, so that he would feel lighter while he ate. The ant took off his jacket and floated away, which taught him a valuable lesson.

# The Chick and
# The Worm

Chick was only three days old and was learning all about the world. Chick came across a worm, who ran away when he saw Chick.

'Hey, there! Why are you running?' asked Chick.

'Because you'll eat me!' exclaimed the worm.

'No! Why would I do that?' asked Chick.

'Because hens eat me!' replied the worm.

Chick and the worm became friends, which bewildered the hens and the roosters. But Chick made them realise that good friendships could be made with anyone!

# The Soup

There were three birds who lived in a tree. 'Let's go and see Đinky Stork. He makes delicious soup,' said one of the birds.

Everyone liked the idea and also invited Fischer, the fox. Inside Đinky's cottage, Đinky prepared the soup for the birds while they chatted at the dining table.

While they waited for the fox, Đinky put the ingredients into a huge pot of boiling water. The birds all stirred it together. They also helped Đinky to lay the table.

The fox had thought that if he arrived early, then he would have to help too, so he had set off late.

When the soup was ready, Đinky served it to the birds. So, by the time the fox arrived, the soup was nearly gone and all that he could do was cry, for being too late.

# The Fighting Cats

There were once two cats, named Etsy and Betsy, who lived near a river bank.

One day, they decided to go fishing. They usually argued a lot, but for once, they decided not to.

They sat on the riverbank. They had some good bait on their fishing rods and caught lots of fish. But soon, Etsy and Betsy began to argue about who had caught the most fish.

A wolf had been watching them and seeing that they were too busy arguing, he grabbed their bucket of fish. He ran off into the forest and left the fighting cats with no fish.

# The Brave Buffalo

It was a hot night and Panzy, the buffalo, couldn't sleep. Seeing that the cow, horse and goat were asleep, Panzy decided to go for a walk.

He stretched his arms and legs and walked under the night sky. Suddenly, he heard the sound of a cockerel crowing.

Panzy was puzzled and thought, 'All of the cockerels are asleep. Who's crowing at this hour?'

The buffalo went to investigate, and saw that three robbers were trying to break into the farmyard.

Panzy bellowed, to wake the farmer, which made the robbers run away. The farmer gave Panzy some apples for scaring them away.

# The Clever Mother Hen

As it was a bright, sunny day, Mother Hen asked her neighbours if they would help her in the wheat field. 'No!' they replied.

So, Mother Hen and her little chicks harvested the wheat and took it to the mill. They returned with a bag of flour. "Who will help me to bake a cake?' she asked.

But once again, they said, 'No!' Mother Hen and her chicks prepared the cake. The sweet smell of the cake attracted the neighbours. They peeped through the window, but this time, Mother Hen did not invite them to eat the cake.

# The Duck Who Wanted to Live on Trees

Leslie Duck was bored with living on the ground. Every other day, there would be paper or empty containers in her nest. 'I don't know who throws rubbish into my nest!' she said, angrily.

She decided to find somewhere else to live and walked round the farm. She went into the chicken coops, horse stables and cow sheds.

'These are not for me,' she muttered.

She looked at the rooftop, but decided that the sun would be too hot for her. Then, she saw a tree.

'Yes! I will live on the tree,' she said.

So, Leslie moved onto the tree.

Everyone talked about the duck who lived on a tree, but she was happy living there.

# The Fox and
# The Turtle

One day, a fox woke up from his afternoon nap. As he was hungry, he walked through the forest in search of food. He came to a river, but he was too lazy to catch fish.

Suddenly, he spotted a turtle near the river. He pounced on the turtle and tried to bite it, but it was too hard.

The turtle smiled and said, 'Why don't you soak me in the river for a while. It will make me soft and then you can take a bite.'

The fox put the turtle into the river. The foolish fox could only stare when the clever turtle swam away. The lazy fox had to go back home, without any food.

# The Bird Who Did Not Want to Fly

Jenny was a little blackbird, who lived on the inside of a chimney, at Lila's house. Lila loved Jenny.

One day, the little bird saw that Lila was packing a bag and asked, 'Are you going somewhere?' 'Yes, I'm going to my friend's pool party,' replied Lila.

Jenny was happy to hear this and went with Lila. Jenny was surprised to see that the pool party was at a swimming pool, as she had never seen one before.

She dipped her wings into the pool and tried to swim too. 'This is much better than flying!' exclaimed Jenny.

She did not want to fly. She enjoyed being at the pool with her friend, Lila and was happy to live in the chimney.

# The Dove and
# The Ant

Tommy, the ant, was once washed into a stream, by heavy rain and didn't know how to swim.

A dove saw him and dropped a leaf into the stream. Tommy climbed onto the leaf and floated to the side. He thanked the dove for his help.

One day, when Tommy was walking through the forest, he saw a hunter aiming his gun at a dove.

When he realised that it was the dove who had saved his life, he bit the hunter's foot. The hunter cried out in pain, which alerted the dove. The dove flew to safety, while the hunter limped back home. The dove flew down to the ant and thanked him. They soon became good friends.

# The Friendly Bird

There was once a poor farmer, who found an injured bird. He took the bird home and nursed it. Then, the poor farmer had some good luck. His cabbages were ready for harvest and made him a lot of money. He bought a hen and a cow with the money and sold the excess eggs and milk. Then, one day, the bird flew away, which made the farmer sad.

The next day, the farmer was surprised to find a silver box on his bed. When he opened it, he found a note inside it. It was from the bird. To thank the farmer for his help, the bird had given him a silver box, full of gemstones.

# The Greedy Squirrel

Macy, the squirrel, was very greedy and would snatch things from her friends. They didn't like her rude behaviour and decided to teach her a lesson.

One day, Macy was collecting nuts, to stock up for the winter. Moly, the monkey approached her.

'Please give me some of your nuts,' said Moly.

Macy gave him two nuts and continued working.

The monkey asked for more nuts, so Macy gave him two more.

But when Moly asked for more nuts, Macy cried, 'No! I have given you more than enough.'

The monkey snatched them from her hand.

'You are so rude!' cried Macy.

But then she realised how her friends felt, when she snatched things from them.

# The Foolish Crocodile

One day, there was a monkey on a tree, who saw a berry bush on the other side of the river. He wanted to go to the other side, but he didn't know how to swim.

Thinking to trick a crocodile into taking him across, he said, 'There's going to be a feast on the other side. I'll get an invitation for you!'

The crocodile agreed and took the monkey across.

When they reached the other side, the monkey ran to the berry bush, shouting, 'There is no feast! I fooled you.'

# The Hen Who Wanted to Hide Her Eggs

Quack-Quack Hen was busy packing for her holiday in Paris. She looked at her eggs.

'Now, I can't take these with me!' she thought.

She went to her friends and asked whether they would look after her eggs.

'We're too busy' they all said.

She was quite worried, but then she spotted a flowerpot. Her face brightened.

'I will hide the eggs in the flowerpot,' she said and then went off on her holiday.

# The Hare and
# The Porcupine

There was once a hare and a porcupine, who lived in a forest. The porcupine challenged the hare to a race. The hare would make fun of the porcupine, calling him sluggish and lazy.

On the day of the race, the hare laughed at the porcupine and said, 'Meet you at the finish line.' The race began. The porcupine ran, but the hare quickly ran past him.

But, when the hare reached the finish line, the porcupine was already there, waiting for him. 'Oh, I think I underestimated the porcupine!' thought the hare. What he didn't know, was that the porcupine at the finish line, was his competitor's twin brother.

# The Ladybug Who Did Not Want Her Spots

Little Dots, the ladybug, had her first day at school. The teacher introduced her to the class and during playtime, Little Dots went to the playground with her classmates.

"Why is her name Little Dots? Whispered Patrick Kangaroo. 'Because of those dirty black spots on her back!' exclaimed Chris Rabbit.

Little Dots started to cry and ran back to the classroom. 'I don't want my spots,' said Little Dots, to her teacher.

When the teacher explained to the class, that lady bugs need their spots, to protect them from predators, they were amazed. Chris Rabbit apologised to Little Dots and she made lots of new friends that day. Every day, she enjoyed going to school and learning new things.

# The Honeybee Who Did Not Want to Make Honey

One day, Buzzy, a honeybee, flew into a classroom and was surprised to see so many children. She sat at the back of the classroom and watched them. She heard them reading out loud and saw them write in their books.

'Wow! This is so interesting and much better than what I do!' she exclaimed. She flew back to the beehive and said, 'Mummy, I don't want to make honey any more. I want to go to school!'

'Honeybees don't go to school,' said Mummy Bee, surprised. Buzzy smiled and said, 'Then, I will be the first bee to do so!' And so, Buzzy went to school and did not make honey any more.

# The Lazy Donkey

There was a merchant, who had two donkeys. He used them alternatively, to carry his goods.

He put bags of salt onto one of the donkeys. The heavy load made the donkey tired and when they came to a river, the donkey fell in it.

When the donkey came out, his load felt lighter. Because the donkey had slipped into the river, the merchant had to go home, where the donkey told the other donkey about the incident.

A couple of days later, the merchant put sacks of cotton onto the other donkey, to sell in the town. They soon came to the river.

Wanting to make his load lighter, the donkey pretended to fall into the river. But when he tried to get out, he couldn't. The cotton had soaked up the water and had made his load heavier.

# The Little, Lost Hedgehog

It was winter and Little Hedgehog was bored. 'You have to stay warm, or you will catch an awful cold,' advised Mama Hedgehog.

But Little Hedgehog stared out of the window. He wanted to play outside. So, when everyone was asleep, he crept out. He ran around and jumped in the snow. He made a big snowman, but soon he was shivering with cold. He wanted to go home, but he was lost.

Little Hedgehog sat under a tree, crying and soon fell asleep. When he woke up, he found himself wrapped in a warm blanket. Mom and Dad Hedgehog had found him and taken him home.

# The Kind Leopard

One day, Leo, the lion, decided to have a race in the jungle, to see which animal was the fastest.

Many animals participated and soon it was the final race between the leopard and the reindeer.

They had to run over the rocky hill, to the other side where the finish line was. The animals cheered for the leopard and the reindeer.

As they were running, the reindeer turned to see where the leopard was and twisted his foot. The kind leopard, picked up the reindeer and carried him to the finish line.

All of the animals were impressed by the leopard's kind gesture.

# The Honourable Monkey

Once upon a time, there was a war against the Fairy Kingdom. The Fairy Queen had been taken hostage by the Goblin King.

A monkey stepped forward, to help the Fairy Queen. 'This is not the way to treat a queen,' he bellowed.

The Goblin King trembled in fear.

'Untie her this instant!' demanded the monkey.

Terrified, he quickly untied her.

'Is this the way you treat a fair lady who has come for peace?' asked the monkey.

When the Goblin King apologised, they signed a peace treaty and all of the fairies thanked the monkey.

# The Lonely Deer

One day, there was a deer who was drinking water at a stream, when it heard a tiger's footsteps. It was so scared that it couldn't think and began to run.

But, instead of running home to safety, the deer ran to a farm, far away. The animals at the farm were not happy to see the deer.

The farmer saw the deer and locked the farm gates, so that it couldn't escape.

The deer felt lonely and homesick. As the days went by, the deer decided that he would return home.

So, one day, when he saw that the farm gate was open, he dashed out and ran all the way home.

# The Lizard Who Was Afraid to Climb the Wall

Lizzy, the baby lizard, lived under a stone with her mother. One day, they received an invitation to visit their aunt, who lived in the city.

Their aunt greeted them at the City Bus Station.

'Come with me,' she said, as she led them to a nearby building.

She climbed on the wall. Her mother followed and then stopped to see that Lizzy was still on the ground.

'What's the matter?' asked her mother.

'I'm too scared to climb the wall!' cried Lizzy.

Her mother smiled and said, 'Don't worry.'

Then, she took Lizzy's hand, but Lizzy was terrified. She was a lizard who was afraid to climb walls.

# The Sheep Who Did Not Want to Give Her Wool

Jt was raining and so, Woolly Sheep read to her babies, a story about Antarctica.

The babies pleaded with her, to take them to Antarctica for a holiday. So, Woolly Sheep began to prepare for their trip.

'We need thick woollens,' she said and then realised that she would need to tell her friends that she wouldn't be able to give them any wool this time.

She went to see Jumpy Kangaroo and Moo-Moo Cow, who were excited to hear about her planned trip to Antarctica. They wished her all the best.

Woolly Sheep and her babies enjoyed their holiday in Antarctica and when they returned home, she shared her adventures with her friends.

# The Monkey's Trick

There were once two cats who were fighting over a slice of cake. To resolve the argument, they asked a monkey to help.

The monkey split the cake into two halves and gave one half to each of them. Just as they were about to eat their cake, the monkey stopped them.

"Wait! Your slice is bigger than her slice!" he said and then took a bite out of the first cat's cake. Then he looked at the cake again. 'This one is now bigger,' he said and took a bite out of the second cat's cake.

The cats watched helplessly, as the monkey continued to eat their cake, until he had eaten it all and there was none left for the cats.

# The Owl Who Wanted to Sleep at Night

Hooty Owl was bored with the dark nights. The stars and moon didn't appeal to him anymore. So, he decided to sleep at night and stay awake during the day.

The next day, he jumped up at the crack of dawn and stood at the window, to admire the sunlight falling into the room. He quickly got dressed and went to Buzzy, the squirrel's treehouse. Buzzy was surprised to see him during the day.

'I want to see what the day is like,' explained Hooty.

'Great! I will show you around,' said Buzzy.

She took Hooty to the park, which he loved. He felt so good, to be out and roam about during the day, and he wanted to be an owl who slept at night.

# The Old Woman
# at the Farm

One day, Woofy Dog took his friends, Woolly Sheep and Cluck-Cluck Hen, to see a special person on the farm.

They went to a small cottage, where they saw an old woman sitting in a rocking chair. She was busy, knitting a sweater. 'Come in!' she said, as she welcomed them into the cottage.

She gave them cups of tea and slices of cake as they chattered. The old woman talked about her life and then it was soon time to leave.

'Do come again,' said the old woman. Woolly and Cluck-Cluck loved her kind face and gentle nature and went back again.